First day of School

LEO DOCI

Copyright © 2024 by Leo Doci

All rights reserved.
No part of this book may be reproduced or used in any manner without written permission of the copyright owner except for the use of quotations in a book review.

First paperback edition 2024

Written by Leo Doci

978-1-80541-529-9 (paperback)
978-1-80541-528-2 (ebook)

It all began a few years ago…

A little child called Leo was standing in the front at the big blue gates frightened, excited and happy holding his mother's hand with all his power.

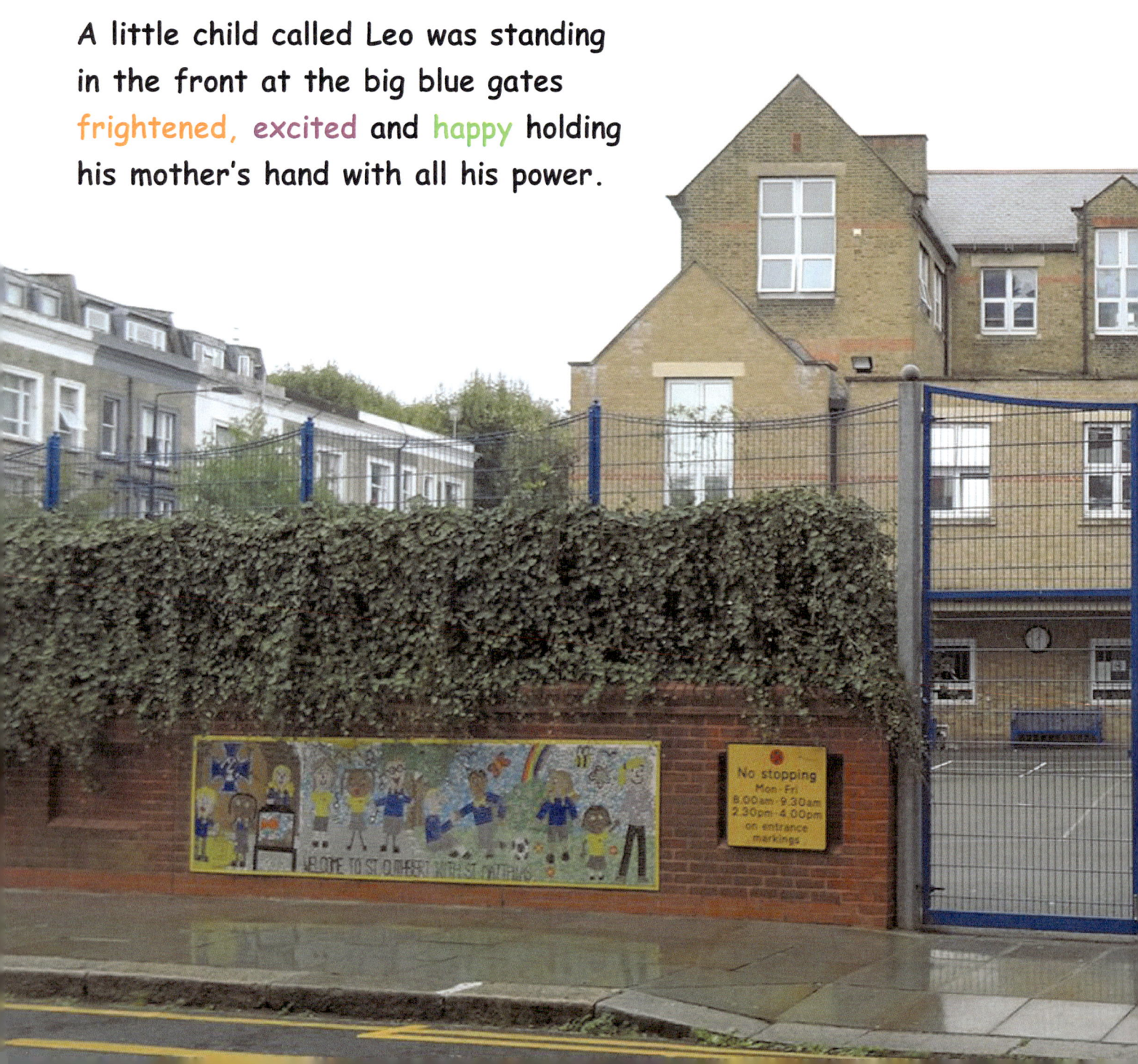

Was Leo's first day of school, the first day of meeting new friends, new teachers and new toys.

Leo was welcomed by this smiling face at the gate, and happy called Miss Putterill.

Leo was invited to the class with other parents and children... He felt shy and happy squeezing even harder his mom's hand.

After some time the teacher invited the parents to leave the school and return later, giving her time to know the children better and go over the day.

Leo felt scared, sad and shy but as the teacher smiled at him he felt very excited about his new adventure.

Excited feeling…..

Happy feeling ...

At the pickup time, Leo was jumping up and down telling his parents how happy he was with his new friends and teacher, and how excited he was for the next day to be back at school.

Leo day by day learnt something new and each day he was telling how happy he was with the school, teachers and friends, but mostly he was happy receiving those golden stickers from Miss Putterill's office.

I have little advice for all the parents, as my mommy did to reassure me with emotions.

Bend down at the child's level and reassure him that will be a fantastic experience for him, and that all he needs to do is enjoy himself.

www.ingramcontent.com/pod-product-compliance
Lightning Source LLC
Chambersburg PA
CBRC091735100526
44585CB00045B/173